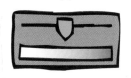

MONSTER ENGLISH

Christabell

HOBBIES	Playing games on her laptop computer
SKILL	Technology whizz
FAVOURITE COLOURS	Pink and red
LIVES	Smile Street with Ezzo, Waldo and Whiffy

Ezzo

HOBBIES	Kung fu
STRENGTH	Martial Arts expert
BEST MOVE	Karate kick
FAVOURITE FILMS	Monster action films

Waldo

FAVOURITE FOOD	Dog biscuits
HOBBIES	Biting squeaky toys
STRANGE FACT	Can change shape
OWNER	Ezzo

Whiffy

FAVOURITE FOOD	Cakes with lots of icing
HOBBIES	Playing, dancing
STRANGE FACT	Turns to invisible vapour when afraid and makes a terrible smell

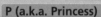

P (a.k.a. Princess)

HOBBIES	Scheming to take over Monster City
STRENGTH	Deadly scream that knocks everybody out
LIKES	Sparkly things, parties

Edgar

HOBBIES	Making machines to take over Monster City
SKILL	Brilliant scientist
BEST INVENTION	Gripping bowtie
BEST FRIEND	P

Flob

HOBBIES	Monster TV
BEST FRIEND	P won't let him have friends, because she doesn't want any
LIKES	Eating yummy food until his tummy is about to pop

E zzo, Christabell, Waldo and Whiffy were standing forlornly in front of the Monster City swimming pool. A 'closed forever' sign had been posted on the door.

Inside, the pool water was now black and oily. Tiles had been smashed and the roof had been ripped open.

"It looks as if someone's used a wrecking ball to ruin the place," Christabell sighed.

"It'll cost a fortune to rebuild this," Ezzo muttered angrily.

That evening, Whiffy and Christabell watched an important announcement on the Monster City TV news together.

"Today the Monster City Science Museum has announced a new invention competition. We interviewed museum boss, Ivor Bigbrain."

An excited looking monster appeared on the screen.

"There'll be a big cash prize for the town or city where the winning inventor lives," Mr Bigbrain explained.

1 Metaphors and similes

Poor Ezzo and Christabell! They had such difficulty explaining how awful the swimming pool looked to their friends, that they had to use similes and metaphors to make their descriptions vivid.

A simile is when you say something is like something else.

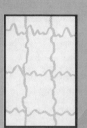

The water was so smooth it was like glass.

A metaphor is when you say something is something else.

The pool was surrounded by mountains of rubble.

2 Root words

If you have to spell complicated words, it can help to know what their roots are. Roots are letter strings that appear in lots of words and have the same basic meanings. We can make lots of different words out of them. For example, the word **phone** comes from the Greek word meaning **voice**.

Telephone

Microphone

Phonetics

Phonics

Christabell is a brilliant inventor, but will she be able to save Monster City swimming pool? Add the first sticker to the picture at the front of the book.

Help describe the swimming pool by completing these sentences. Write M next to the sentences that contain metaphors and S next to the sentences that contain similes.

1   Before the disaster, the water in the pool was as clear as _____. ____

2   The water was as oily as _____. ____

3   The piles of rubble were _____. ____

4   When Christabell saw what had happened, she went as pale as _____. ____

5   _____ of tiles and bricks lay everywhere. ____

6   The holes in the roof were as jagged as _____. ____

7   The water was as black as _____. ____

8   The smashed tiles were _____. ____

9   Christabell could swim like _____. ____

10 The broken lights were dangling _____ from the ceiling. ____

11 The broken windows were _____ in the walls. ____

12 "Whoever did this had a heart of _____," said Ezzo. ____

13 Ezzo went as red as _____ with anger. ____

14 The drained pool was a _____. ____

15 Ezzo was as angry as a _____. ____

The trouble with Ivor Bigbrain was that he liked to use long, complicated words whenever he could. Christabell and Ezzo understood him, but they had to explain what he said to Whiffy. Match the word roots with their meanings by drawing a line.

1   two
2   study
3   hear
4   air
5   fear
6   water
7   before
8   self
9   believe
10 to write
11 first
12 greater
13 three
14 to write
15 across

aqua   phobia   bi   super   audio   ology   aero   trans   cred   prim   scribe   tri   graph   auto   pre

The TV announcer continued: "In Monster City we've high hopes of winning the money, with our famous Smile Street science whizz, Christabell. We'll be using the prize to build a new swimming pool."

"What? I haven't even entered!" Christabell said, startled.

"But you could win easily! Think of the little monsters that love swimming. You could fund a new pool for them!" Whiffy urged her.

The TV announcer cut in with some more information: "Deadlines are very tight for entering the competition. All competitors need to start work straight away."

At that moment Ezzo walked in. "Are you ready to go skateboarding, Christabell? I hoped we could talk about my birthday party, too," he said, looking expectantly at her.

"Sorry, Ezzo. I'll have to miss the skateboarding. I've got to get inventing," Christabell replied apologetically.

"Okay, that's cool," Ezzo shrugged. "We can do it tomorrow."

Christabell rushed off to start work on some prize-winning ideas.

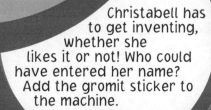

Christabell has to get inventing, whether she likes it or not! Who could have entered her name? Add the gromit sticker to the machine.

3 Language

When Ezzo came in, he gave Christabell a leaflet about the competition, which had the headline 'Be a brainbox and earn some monster cash!' He also gave her an official entry form, entitled 'Official Rules for Entry into the Monster City Inventing Competition'. Whiffy thought it was odd that the two pieces of literature were so different, with one being so friendly and one being so formal.

4 Spelling

Christabell's first idea for an invention was for a machine that would help monsters to spell. It is important to get your spelling right, so people (or monsters) understand exactly what you mean.

These sentences are from the flyer and the entry form. Write formal or informal by each one.

1   Each inventor, or team, may enter only one invention.   _____

2   Calling All Inspired Inventors!!!   _____

3   Rules may be obtained from the Science Museum by post or in person.   _____

4   All entries become the property of the Science Museum.   _____

5   Entry is FREE! That's right, it won't cost you diddly!!!   _____

6   Entry forms from the Science Museum.   _____

7   Make your mind work for you.   _____

8   The competition will be judged by Ivor Bigbrain and his decision is final.   _____

9   To Whom It May Concern: _____

10   Win a HUGE CASH PRIZE for your town!!!   _____

11   I hereby confirm that I have read the rules and have followed them all.   _____

12   Competition is FREE FREE FREE to enter!!!   _____

13   Are YOU an invento-maniac????   _____

14   I certify that this invention is all my own work.   _____

15   Enter now!!!   _____

Put the following incorrectly spelt words through the machine, then write them correctly.

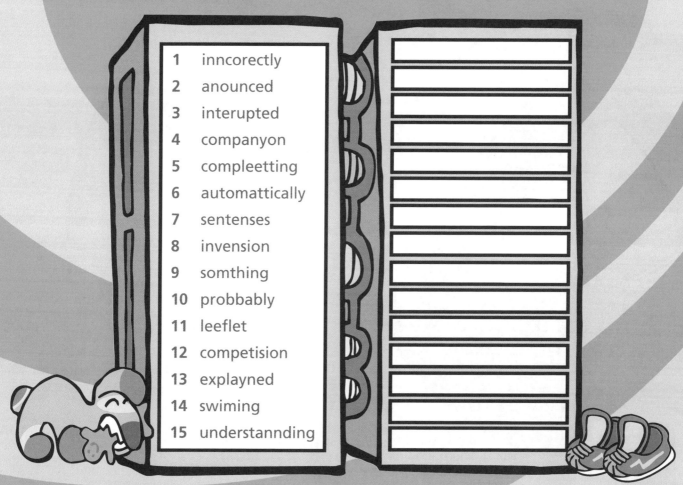

1   inncorectly

2   anounced

3   interupted

4   companyon

5   compleetting

6   automattically

7   sentenses

8   invension

9   somthing

10   probbably

11   leeflet

12   competision

13   explayned

14   swiming

15   understannding

All day she stayed in her room, working on her computer, trying to design a spectacular new invention. Meanwhile, Whiffy raced round to the Monster City Science Museum to collect a set of competition rules.

"There are loads of them!" he warned when he returned, carrying a book as thick as a doorstep, full of strict rules for entries.

"They must be joking!" Christabell gasped. It took her an hour just to read through them.

The next day, Ezzo knocked on her door. "Do you want to go skateboarding?" he asked.

"Sorry, I can't," Christabell replied. "I've got to get my invention finished, to win the money for the swimming pool. We'll have to do it tomorrow."

"No problem. Let me know if I can help," Ezzo smiled. Just then Whiffy arrived with yet another book of competition rules.

"They've added lots of new ones about what you can and can't invent," he announced.

"Oh no!" Christabell frowned. "What's Ivor Bigbrain playing at?" After she read the new rules she had to start all over again.

Poor Christabell – geniuses don't need rules! It will be worth the hard work when the little monsters have a swimming pool. Pop on your setting dial.

5 Comprehension

It is important to read instructions carefully, to make sure you understand them.

The Science Museum Invention Competition Rules (New)

1 Read the rules and bin them.
2 Put signed invention plan in an envelope. Attach name and address label with sticky tape, not glue.
3 Entries must fit into a crate 3m long × 2m deep × 3m wide, unless you have special permission for a larger entry – write to us for Form 5QXb1.
4 Use glow in the dark ink to label buttons on your entry.
5 Instructions must be typed in English on white paper.
6 Spend no more than 500 Doobreys and put all signed receipts in the envelope with your entry form.

6 Proof-reading

It's very important to check your work thoroughly before you let anyone else see it.

This is called proof-reading.

Christabell always checks her work through thoroughly to make sure her inventions will be perfect!

Help Christabell understand the rules by following the instructions below.

1. Put a star by the point that tells you what to use to attach the label to your entry.

2. Circle the maximum size for an entry.

3. What must you do with the rules, once they have been read? Underline the words.

4. Draw a circle round the colour paper you must use.

5. What number is the permission slip? Underline it.

6. Put a note saying 'borrow money from Ezzo' next to the point that tells you how much you can spend.

7. What must be labelled with glow in the dark ink? Underline the word.

8. Put a note saying 'send off today' next to the point that tells you what to do if your entry is extra-large.

9. Put a cross by the two things you should sign.

10. Put a tick by the point that tells you what to do, once you have read the rules.

11. Draw an arrow pointing to the language your instructions must be typed in.

12. Draw an arrow pointing to the kind of ink you must use for labelling buttons.

13. Cross out the words that tell you what you must not use to attach your label to your invention.

14. Draw a circle around the number of the point that tells you how to get Form 5QXb1.

15. Draw a wavy line under the item that must be attached to your invention with sticky tape.

No wonder Christabell was having trouble understanding the second set of rules – they were full of spelling and grammar mistakes. Underline the mistakes in these sentences, then write the correct version over it in a coloured pen, like a teacher marking work.

1. Ecstra Siense Musuem Invention Compitition Rules

2. These are the knew extra rules of the competition Follow them or you're entrey will be disquallified.

3. Your entry mUst fall into one of these groups: Making Things; Art Transport; Having Fun; Doing Boring Things For Us; Food and Drink; Helping The Enviroment.

4. Their are specail rules for each catagory. Folow them or els!

5. Inventions what make thing must use recycleable materials. The inventeon must be biger than whatever it makes.

6. Art Includes panting, sculbting, writting and musick. Any other kind of art comes under Having Fun, unless it's borring or sad, when it will be disqalified.

7. the art your Invension made must make people happy, or it will be dissqualified.

8. All kinds of transport is aloud, accept those that takes people to impossable places like over the rainbow.

9. if You invention goes so faster it make the judges sick, or so slow the fall asleep, it will be disqualified.

10. Having Fun can incclude anything you licke, but if the judges get borred, your invention will be disqualified.

11. Doing Boring Things For Us include housework, homework ect, but only the borin kinds. If the judges doesn't think your invention does somthing boring, it will be disqualified.

12. Food and Drink includes mashines that grow food, invent rescipes or cook. The judges will taist the food. If they dye of food poisening, your invention will be disqualified.

13. Helping the Envirement. Thiss includes inventions that recicle materials, Cut waste or help people save energy. If the judges waste a lot of enurgy unnderstanding your invention, it will be disqualified.

14. You will loose marx if you bore the judges.

15. No bribury alowed. Not even choclate. Rilly.

As Ezzo wandered away to skateboard on his own, somebody was spying on the goings-on in Smile Street. Edgar was hidden inside a parked van, looking through the van walls with his x-ray glasses, occasionally glancing at a computer monitor next to him. He was working some remote controls to move a robot rat he'd invented. It was close to the Smile Street gang's house and sending back pictures and sound.

"So far, so good. It's time for phase two of my plan," Edgar chuckled nastily.

Ezzo was skateboarding in the park that same afternoon, when Christabell appeared.

"Hi!" he grinned. "Have you finished your invention?"

"Oh, that. I don't think I'll bother," Christabell replied.

"But what about the money for the new swimming pool?" Ezzo asked, surprised, but Christabell just shrugged.

"Are you okay?" Ezzo asked, staring at her. "You seem..."

"Back off, Ezzo! Don't criticise me!" Christabell snapped angrily.

Ezzo finds Christabell's behaviour very strange. It doesn't seem like her at all! Add the cloud squashing funnel.

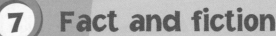

7 Fact and fiction

A fact is a piece of true information.

An opinion is what a person thinks about something. Someone else might disagree.

Fiction is a made-up story.

8 Crosswords

Crosswords are fun word games. They interconnect words which you add into a grid.

Ezzo didn't do a good job of persuading Christabell to work on her machine. Maybe if he'd used more interesting words, he would have done better.

Crosswords are good ways to learn new words and to make you think about how to use them.

Edgar's nasty plan nearly came unstuck, because his robot rat started sending back the wrong information – it was getting facts, opinion, and fiction (from its built-in library of nasty fairy stories) mixed up. Write Fact, Opinion or Fiction next to each sentence.

1   Clones look just like their original. _____

2   Once upon a time there was a girl called Snow White
    who had a wicked step-mother. _____

3   "You shall go to the ball," said the Fairy Godmother
    to Cinderella. _____

4   Robots are not alive. _____

5   Christabell seems kinder than P. _____

6   Cameras are used to take photographs. _____

7   Skateboarding is fun. _____

8   Televisions need electricity to work. _____

9   The Gingerbread Boy laughed and ran out of the door. _____

10 Real rats are small furry animals. _____

11 You should be nice to your friends. _____

12 Jack planted the bean and in the morning a giant
    a giant beanstalk had grown from it. _____

13 Museums are interesting. _____

14 Goldilocks fell fast asleep on the bed. _____

15 Fighting is wrong. _____

Complete this crossword to learn some unusual words. Pick words from the list to complete the crossword. The Across answers mean the opposite of the clues. The Down answers mean the same as the clues. The words in the box will help you fill in the answers. You won't need all of them!

wise silly truthful despairing artistic gratitude tough resent grumpy generous
spite caring dishonest unhelpful intelligence placid kind daft cheerful

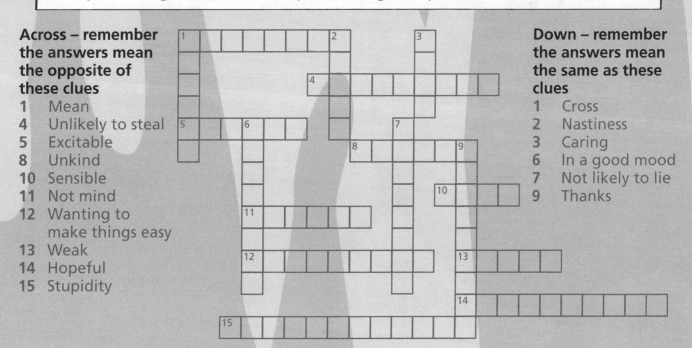

Across – remember the answers mean the opposite of these clues

1   Mean
4   Unlikely to steal
5   Excitable
8   Unkind
10 Sensible
11 Not mind
12 Wanting to
    make things easy
13 Weak
14 Hopeful
15 Stupidity

Down – remember the answers mean the same as these clues

1   Cross
2   Nastiness
3   Caring
6   In a good mood
7   Not likely to lie
9   Thanks

"**S**orry!" Ezzo replied, amazed. Christabell had never spoken to him like that before. Just then Waldo came trotting up to them, but when he saw Christabell he growled and flattened his ears.

"You should control your pet better," Christabell sneered.

"What's eating you, exactly?" Ezzo gasped.

"You're so selfish. I suppose you want me to do all the work for your stupid birthday party. Well, I'm not going to," Christabell shouted and stomped off, leaving Ezzo open-mouthed and upset.

He sat unhappily in the park, wondering what he'd done to irritate Christabell.

Edgar sat in his van, watching him on the monitor. "Go in now," he radioed to P. A few minutes later she appeared in the park.

"Ezzo, you look unhappy. Can I help?" P cooed. Ezzo turned away, but she sat down next to him.

"It's your birthday soon, isn't it? I could help you plan a party. I'm good at that sort of thing," P smiled. "Don't you think it's time we stopped fighting and became friends?"

9 Sayings

Every country has common sayings that sum up certain situations so well that everyone knows and uses them. Be careful not to use them too often though!

"Sticks and stones will break my bones, but names will never hurt me," Ezzo thought after Christabell had gone.

10 Letters

It's important to make sure your letters are always neat and use correct spellings, so the person you are writing to understands what you are telling them.

After Christabell left, Ezzo decided to write her a letter, but he was so upset that he made lots of spelling mistakes.

Something very odd is going on, if P is being nice to one of the Smile Street Gang! Put on the baddie sensing detector, that will get rid of her!.

Here are some other famous sayings. Draw a line to complete them.

1 A bird in the hand is worth
2 People who live in glass houses
3 Familiarity breeds
4 Absence makes the heart
5 Out of sight,
6 He who hesitates is
7 If you make your bed,
8 A rose by any other name would smell
9 You might as well be hanged for a sheep
10 In for a penny, in for
11 Look before
12 A friend in need is
13 Cut your coat according to
14 Better late
15 The early bird catches

a contempt.
b you must lie in it.
c you leap.
d two in the bush.
e shouldn't throw stones.
f as for a lamb.
g the worm.
h grow fonder.
i your cloth.
j out of mind.
k than never.
l lost.
m a pound.
n a friend indeed.
o as sweet.

Help Ezzo by finding the spelling mistakes. There are fifteen. Underline them, then write them correctly underneath.

Dear Christabell,

I'm writting to you because I'm very unhappy about what just hapened wile I was skatebording. I can see that I probibly upset you somehow, but I don't know what I did rong. Whatever it was, I don't think you should have been so narsty to me. You could just have asked me to say sory. I'm shure you know I would have. We hav been freinds for a long time and I hope we can stil be, but not if you keep shouting at me and being rude like that. It really isn't fair. In fact, I think you shood apoligise to me.

Your pal,

Ezzo

Write the correct spellings here:

1 _____
2 _____
3 _____
4 _____
5 _____

6 _____
7 _____
8 _____
9 _____
10 _____

11 _____
12 _____
13 _____
14 _____
15 _____

P patted Ezzo's hand and handed him a card.

"Here's my mobile number. Phone me if you need help. I'll be there for you," she assured him and walked away, waving back at him as if they were best buddies. Ezzo walked home feeling very confused. P was being nice to him and Christabell was being horrible. It didn't make sense. To confuse him further, when he arrived home Christabell was waiting for him.

"I've finished my invention," she smiled.

"Bully for you," he replied, thinking that at least she could say sorry for being mean earlier.

"Don't you want to see it?" Christabell asked, shocked at Ezzo's surly expression.

"Actually, I don't think I do," he muttered, turning his back on her and walking away. Inside his van, Edgar was watching, listening and laughing loudly. But outside in Smile Street, Whiffy and Waldo were puzzled and dismayed to see their friends fall out.

"We have to find out what's going on," Whiffy whispered to Waldo, who nudged at Whiffy with his nose to make him follow.

Whiffy and Waldo know something is amiss if friends like Ezzo and Christabell are falling out. What will they find out? Add the cloud monitor device.

(11) Weighing things up

When coming to conclusions, we need to make sure we weigh things up by the facts, not by opinion. An opinion is not a fact – it's just what one person thinks.

When someone is trying to be fair, they use phrases like 'on the one hand' and 'then again', which show they are trying to see things from the other person's point of view.

(12) Conjunctions

If Ezzo had known Edgar was up to something, he might have behaved differently, **but** he didn't, **so** he just thought Christabell was acting strangely. Ezzo thought hard about the way Christabell was behaving, **but** it didn't make much sense.

There are lots of different words you can use to join parts of sentences together. They include **if**, **and**, **or**, **but** and **because**, though there are many others. They all mean slightly different things.

Ezzo was so upset that he decided to write down what had happened. Underline the parts that show that Ezzo was trying to be fair in black. Underline the parts where Ezzo says why he and Christabell should be friends in blue. Underline the parts where Ezzo says that Christabell is behaving badly in red. Put a circle round any words or phrases that show that Ezzo is just stating his opinion.

Until today, Christabell and I have always been good friends. She has always been on my side in fights, especially with P and Edgar. I think we have a lot in common, even though she likes working on her computer and I like skateboarding and stuff like that. We like the same kind of jokes, and we both like Whiffy and Waldo. It seems to me that nothing has happened to change any of that.

However, I'm not sure Christabell agrees with me. On one hand, she was really rude and mean to me when I saw her in the park. I can't think why she would call me selfish for wanting help with my party, when I don't think she has been selfish working on her invention. Then again, maybe she was just in a bad mood or something, because she seemed okay when I spoke to her just now!

Tick the sentence in each pair which sounds best or makes most sense.

1. ☐ Christabell and Ezzo were good friends, and she started being nasty to him.
   ☐ Christabell and Ezzo were good friends, but she started being nasty to him.

2. ☐ If Ezzo is hurt, he should say so.   ☐ Ezzo is hurt, then he should say so.

3. ☐ Ezzo saw Christabell in the park, so she was with some new friends.
   ☐ When Ezzo saw Christabell in the park, she was with some new friends.

4. ☐ Christabell was friendly, then she changed.
   ☐ Christabell was friendly, and she changed.

5. ☐ Either something is wrong with Christabell, or Ezzo is imagining things.
   ☐ Either something is wrong with Christabell, but Ezzo is imagining things.

6. ☐ If Ezzo is sad, he sulks.   ☐ If Ezzo is sad, because he sulks.

7. ☐ Ezzo stormed out, so he was upset.   ☐ Ezzo stormed out, because he was upset.

8. ☐ Ezzo was upset, but he stormed out.   ☐ Ezzo was upset, so he stormed out.

9. ☐ Ezzo didn't want to argue, so he ran off.
   ☐ Ezzo didn't want to argue, then he ran off.

10. ☐ Christabell wanted to show Ezzo her invention, but he slammed the door.
    ☐ Christabell wanted to show Ezzo her invention, until he slammed the door.

11. ☐ Christabell saw Ezzo while he was skateboarding in the park.
    ☐ If Christabell saw Ezzo, he was skateboarding in the park.

12. ☐ When Ezzo got home, he was still angry.   ☐ Ezzo got home, but he was still angry.

13. ☐ As Christabell spoke to Ezzo, she realised he was annoyed with her.
    ☐ Christabell spoke to Ezzo, therefore she realised he was annoyed with her.

14. ☐ If Christabell was inventing, Ezzo was skateboarding in the park.
    ☐ While Christabell was inventing, Ezzo was skateboarding in the park.

15. ☐ Ezzo was hurt, but he smiled bravely.   ☐ Ezzo was hurt, because he smiled bravely.

Waldo led Whiffy towards the Science Museum.

"Is there something in there?" Whiffy asked. Waldo barked.

"Okay, but I'll have to turn to invisible smelly vapour to go in there secretly. You'll have to scare me," Whiffy suggested. Waldo growled at him.

"That's not scary enough," Whiffy shook his head. Suddenly Waldo changed shape. He grew as big as a lion and roared at Whiffy, showing a set of fangs. Whiffy immediately went invisible, which also made a terrible smell that made Waldo run away.

Whiffy crept invisibly into the Science Museum. When he turned a corner he saw a familiar face. Flob was loading something into a box.

"Aargh! Gross!" Flob choked, as Whiffy's nasty smell overwhelmed him. He knocked over the box, and photographs spilt out onto the floor as he stumbled off. Whiffy picked up some of the photos as possible evidence. Then he moved towards an office door marked 'Ivor Bigbrain' and turned the handle. A big surprise was inside.

13 More spelling

Whiffy decided to write down what he saw in the museum. He wanted to spell everything correctly.

Not all spellings follow rules. There are some common spellings that you just have to learn.

science   appl**iance**

14 Prefixes and suffixes

Prefixes are letter strings that are added to the beginning of a word. They change its meaning.

understand
misunderstand

Suffixes are letter strings that are added to the end of a word to change its meaning.

scorn

scorn**ful**

Whiffy's smell can come in very handy. I wonder what the surprise can be! Pop on the electronic doodah compressor.

Whiffy was so nervous that he made lots of spelling mistakes. Help him by underlining the correctly spelt words in these groups. Watch out for the vowels in the middle!

1 seperate   separate   sepirate

2 telephone   telophone   telaphone

3 disippear   disappear   disuppear

4 librery   librury   library

5 probably   probibly   probebly

6 important   importent   importunt

7 garige   garuge   garage

8 pleasent   pleasant   pleasunt

9 fasten   fastin   fastun

10 necklice   necklace   necklece

11 eliphant   elephant   eluphant

12 fashin   fashon   fashion

13 brother   brothur   brothor

14 seventy   sevinty   sevunty

15 necissary   necessary   necassary

Help Whiffy remember what he saw in the museum by completing these words. They are all words he read in the museum. Use the prefixes and suffixes in the box to help you. You might end up with the same word more than once!

| tele-   sub-   con-   -ology   micro-   ex-   de- |
| mis-   -port   -ject   com-   oct-   in- |

1 _____phone   _____scope

   _____behave

2 _____vert   _____ober   _____ject

3 _____tract   _____scribe

   _____taken

4 _____scope   _____marine

   im_____

5 re_____   _____puter   _____agon

6 _____port   _____gram   _____bine

7 _____tect   _____et   _____tract

8 techn_____   _____place in_____

9 sup_____   _____pect   _____light

10 _____hear   _____mon   _____part

11 _____port   _____erable

    _____pete

12 _____stance   _____plete

    _____opus

13 psych_____   _____side   bi_____

14 _____fide   _____sume   _____pert

15 _____graph   _____pend

    _____fort

Back in Smile Street, Ezzo was aimlessly skateboarding around. Christabell was hidden inside the house, feverishly drawing up yet another invention after more rule changes. Ezzo was glum and Christabell was tired and upset. Smile Street was not a happy place, as Edgar could see. He used his x-ray glasses to check on Christabell working and his remote-controlled robot spy rat for footage of Ezzo. The rat was sitting near Ezzo now, filming him.

Suddenly Whiffy and Waldo rushed around the corner. Waldo barked when he saw the robot rat. Edgar had to frantically work his remote controls to make it scuttle away. Whiffy pulled Ezzo's arm excitedly.

"Come with me!" he begged.

Ezzo sprinted after Whiffy in the direction of the Science Museum, but stopped dead when he saw Christabell walking along with a group of new friends, ignoring him!

"I thought she was in the house..." Ezzo began, puzzled.

"Don't worry about that now!" Whiffy interrupted, dragging him to the museum.

15 Connectives

Connectives are words or phrases that join parts of sentences together.

Some of the sentences Christabell wrote to make her invention used connectives of position: Push the red button **below** the green dial.

Some used connectives of sequence: **Secondly**, push the red button.

Finally, some used connectives of logic: The power isn't switched on, **so** the machine doesn't work.

16 Irregular verbs

Waldo and Whiffy **had** to show Ezzo what they'd **found** in the Science Museum, before he **would** believe them.

It was all very irregular – but then, so are these verbs in bold!

Irregular verbs are the ones that don't have **ed** added to them when you put them in the past tense.

Edgar knows that Christabell is the gadget queen, which is why he keeps a firm eye on her. Add the cloud trapping apparatus.

Read these sentences and decide what kind of connectives they use. Underline the connective. Write P for position, S for sequence or L for logic next to each sentence.

1   Turn the large handle five times, then press the blue button.

2   Carry the bottle of liquid carefully so it doesn't spill.

3   Make sure the squasher goes up and down when you turn the handle.

4   Stand the machine on a firm surface.

5   Connect the tubes firmly or the machine won't work.

6   Next, set the dial to 'maximum'.

7   Beside the green button there is a purple dial.

8   Push the tube in so it's firmly connected.

9   If the machine doesn't work, check the tubes.

10 Keep a mop by the machine.

11 Point the funnel at the sky.

12 Empty the tank when it gets more than half full.

13 After you have put the plug in the socket, turn the machine on.

14 Put the bucket under the pipe.

15 Finally, watch the machine work.

Look at this breakdown of recent events in Monster City that uses irregular verbs. They are in the present tense. Put them in the past tense instead.

1   Edgar **winds** the film back because it **is** finished. _____

2   He **takes** some more pictures with a new film. _____

3   He **drinks** some coffee while he waits for Christabell and Ezzo
    to come out. _____

4   Christabell **thinks** her invention **will** work eventually. _____

5   Whiffy **does** not like going into the Science Museum alone. _____

6   Waldo **creeps** along behind him. _____

7   Their feet **slide** on the polished floor _____

8   The museum **teaches** people about interesting things. _____

9   Ivor Bigbrain's voice **rises** to a shriek when he **tells** them what
    P and Edgar did. _____

10 He **shakes** with anger. _____

11 He **writes** a letter to the mayor about it. _____

12 When she finishes inventing, Christabell **sleeps**. _____

13 The trouble **is**, the rules **keep** changing. _____

14 They **say** her invention **will** be disqualified if she **does** not obey
    the rules. _____

15 Christabell **is** not the kind of person who **breaks** rules for fun. _____

Inside the museum, visitors were crowding round a display entitled 'Photography explained. Let us take your photo'. Each visitor sat on a stool. A camera flashed and took their portrait.

"Look at these." Whiffy thrust the photos that Flob had dropped earlier into Ezzo's hands.

"That's weird. These show the new friends we've just seen Christabell with," Ezzo remarked.

"Exactly!" Whiffy said triumphantly.

He led Ezzo to Ivor Bigbrain's office. When they flung open the door they found the museum boss tied up and gagged in the corner.

"I found him earlier, but I couldn't do anything. P came in with another Ivor Bigbrain."

"What?" Ezzo asked.

"Grmmmmm," the tied-up Ivor Bigbrain cried through his gag. Ezzo freed him.

"They're cloning everyone in Monster City!' Ivor explained. "The clones are mean and horrible, and obey P and Edgar. The camera is really a cloning machine. It clones everyone who gets their photo taken."

A cloning machine! Edgar has devised his own invention, but his is to rule Monster City, not help the little monsters get a new swimming pool! Pop on the funnel.

17 Using dictionaries

A dictionary lists words in alphabetical order, with their meanings, like this:

Astronomy – the study of space, the planets and stars.

Some words have more than one meaning.

Bear – a large wild animal that is found in North America and in zoos; to carry something.

Cricket – a game using a bat and ball; an insect like a grasshopper.

18 Languages

Many strange-looking words come from languages other than English, such as Italian, Dutch and Indian. Sometimes, they have even odder plurals that don't follow the usual words, so you just need to learn them.

While Ezzo was walking through the museum, he saw displays with a lot of words he didn't quite understand. They are written underneath. There are two possible meanings for each word, but only one is correct! Put a tick by the correct meaning.

1 skull
   a ○ to row
   b ○ the bones in your head

2 lobster
   a ○ a fish with a shell and claws
   b ○ someone who throws something

3 steam engine
   a ○ a machine that works using steam
   b ○ to clean with steam

4 freezing point
   a ○ an icicle
   b ○ the temperature at which water turns to ice

5 bacteria
   a ○ a kind of frog
   b ○ tiny little animals

6 fingernail
   a ○ a claw
   b ○ a spiral

7 gravity
   a ○ the force that makes things fall down
   b ○ digging a grave

8 solar system
   a ○ a way of making electricity from sunlight
   b ○ our sun and the planets go round it

9 android
   a ○ a hand towel
   b ○ a robot that looks like a person

10 pendulum
   a ○ a weight on a string
   b ○ a pen with a broken nib

11 aardvark
   a ○ a South American animal
   b ○ a burp

12 friction
   a ○ a story
   b ○ what happens when two objects rub against each other

13 observatory
   a ○ a building used for watching the stars
   b ○ looking at the ground

14 jet
   a ○ a black cat
   b ○ an engine

15 chemist
   a ○ a shoe that comes up to the ankle
   b ○ someone who studies what things are made of

Write a sentence using each word. Use a dictionary if you are unsure.

1 ☐ spaghetti _____
2 ☐ scissors _____
3 ☐ ravioli _____
4 ☐ antennae _____
5 ☐ data _____
6 ☐ bacteria _____
7 ☐ fish _____
8 ☐ mice _____
9 ☐ phenomena _____
10 ☐ trousers _____
11 ☐ criteria _____
12 ☐ fungi _____
13 ☐ wolves _____
14 ☐ bungalow _____
15 ☐ dice _____

The office door opened and the Ivor Bigbrain clone marched in with other cloned monsters, who frowned and looked evil. They moved in on the goodies, but Ezzo took a flying leap through the air and kicked them down like skittles. Soon he had them all tied up on the floor.

"I saw you on TV, announcing the competition," Whiffy remarked to the real Ivor Bigbrain. "I've never been on TV," Ivor insisted. "That was my clone. The competition is all a trick!"

Ezzo and Whiffy rushed back to Smile Street, where Christabell was working on her invention at the front of the house, her hands covered in oil. "How do I know you're the real Christabell?" Ezzo quizzed.

"I beg your pardon?" Christabell replied, puzzled.

"Would you help someone across the road?" Ezzo asked knowingly.

"Of course!" Christabell insisted.

"Would you look after Whiffy if he was sick?" Ezzo added.

"Yes!" Christabell nodded.

"Then you're not a horrible clone!" Ezzo declared and hugged her.

(19) non-fiction

A letter is a written communication that's usually sent by post. It may use formal or informal language.

An article is a written piece for a magazine or newspaper that usually includes both fact and personal opinion.

A flyer is a piece of printed matter to anybody who reads it. that's used to advertise an event, person or product.

article   flyer   letter

(20) Conditional words

Poor Ezzo was terribly confused. If this was the real Christabell, then maybe everything was okay – but perhaps that was just a clone.

Conditional words help us to think and write about ideas that may or may not be true. They include words such as **if**, **perhaps** and **maybe**.

now that Ezzo and Christabell are friends again, they can give P and Edgar a run for their money. Add the battery sticker to the machine.

Here is a list of features you might find in non-fiction writing. Decide where you would find each feature. Write L for letter, A for article or F for flyer next to each feature. There may be more than one.

1   sentence fragments   _____

2   caption   _____

3   address   _____

4   bullet points   _____

5   headline   _____

6   unusual punctuation (e.g. extra exclamation marks)   _____

7   date   _____

8   salutation (Dear)   _____

9   different fonts   _____

10 quotes   _____

11 complicated layout (the way the words look on the page)   _____

12 signature   _____

13 sub-heading   _____

14 slang   _____

15 written in the first person   _____

Complete the sentences below using conditional words and phrases from the box. Add punctuation, such as commas, if needed.

if   would   perhaps   should   could   might

1   Ezzo thought he would scream _____ Christabell was nasty to him again.

2   The real Christabell _____ never be mean to anyone.

3   _____ Ezzo believe Christabell?

4   P _____ be angry when she finds out.

5   _____ P's plan was a bad one.

6   Christabell _____ tell that Ezzo was puzzled.

7   _____ Whiffy is scared he will go invisible.

8   _____ Edgar took a picture of Christabell.

9   If Christabell and Ezzo hurry, they _____ get to the museum in time.

10 Christabell will be nasty to Ezzo _____ she is a clone.

11 Whiffy wondered what he _____ do next.

12 Ivor Bigbrain _____ help get rid of the clones.

13 Edgar _____ be able to tell where Whiffy is because of the smell.

14 When P meets Edgar _____ they will argue.

15 If P had her way, she _____ be in charge.

C hristabell showed her friends her new invention.

"It's a 'get rid of black clouds' machine. It might not win the competition, but it will make your birthday sunny, Ezzo."

"You're a wonderful friend," Ezzo grinned. "But the competition is a fake. The palace monsters trashed the pool, then set it up. They knew it would keep you out of the way." Just then Waldo trotted in, carrying Edgar's robot spy rat in his mouth.

"So that's how they kept an eye on us," Ezzo gasped.

"You think you're so clever," a cynical voice scoffed behind them. They swung round to see the Christabell clone, along with clones of Ezzo, Whiffy and Waldo!

"Edgar took your photos with his robot rat. He fed it into his cloning machine and here we are!" the Whiffy clone giggled. "Though I don't smell as disgusting as you," it pointed at poor Whiffy.

"That's mean!" Whiffy cried.

"Good!" the Whiffy clone sneered.

The Ezzo clone menacingly cracked the joints of his fingers one by one.

21 Connectives

Something was wrong with Christabell's invention! It really wasn't working as well as it should. She wrote down a description of what it was supposed to do. Help her out with it by putting in the correct connective words from the list supplied.

because however
despite so next but
since then therefore
otherwise unless
furthermore if which
first and although
when

22 Point of view

The clones are really mean! If they were the heroes of this story, maybe they wouldn't seem so bad.

Most stories are told through the point of view of one of the characters. That means the writer says everything as if that character was seeing or hearing it. Usually, that helps readers understand how that character feels about things.

The clones are a nasty bunch, but what would you expect from Edgar! Put the pipe sticker in the right place.

Complete these sentences using connective words from the list supplied.

1 _____ my machine is to work properly, all the pieces must be connected correctly.

2 _____, the big tank must be large enough.

3 _____, it mustn't have any holes in it.

4 _____, it has to stand firmly on the ground, _____ it could also be held on a stand.

5 _____ it is a machine for getting rid of black clouds, it must have a Black Cloud Detector.

6 The detector is on the front of the machine _____ it is easy to read.

7 It must be kept clean, _____ it will not work properly.

8 _____ the machine detects black clouds, the Black Cloud Sucker turns on automatically.

9 There is a Cloud-Squasher in the tank _____ goes up and down, _____ the handle on the side of the tank is turned.

10 _____ the handle is turned too fast, the Cloud-Squasher will jam.

11 _____ the tank is emptied regularly, it will leak.

12 Unsquashed clouds are bigger than squashed ones, _____ the Cloud Sucker tube is larger than the tank emptying tubes.

13 Both tubes must be cleaned regularly – _____ they will get gummed up.

14 _____ all of these jobs are as important as each other, _____ they are all necessary to make the machine work.

15 _____, remember to turn the machine off in hot weather, or it will overheat.

First underline the part of the sentence that tells you it's from Christabell's point of view. Then rewrite it underneath from her clone's point of view.

1 Ezzo, Whiffy, Waldo and I stood talking in Smile Street, when our clones arrived.

2 _____

3 "You think you're so clever," a cynical voice said from behind them.

4 _____

5 We swung round and saw our clones, who stood sneering at us.

6 _____

7 I wondered how they could look so like us and yet look so mean.

8 _____

9 I stood up a bit straighter and got ready to pull my comb out of my pocket.

10 _____

11 "Edgar took your photos with his robot rat. He fed them into his cloning machine and here we are!" Whiffy's clone giggled.

12 _____

13 The clone pointed at poor Whiffy. "Though I don't smell as disgusting as you."

14 _____

15 Christabell scowled. The clones really were horrible.

The Christabell clone whipped a sharpened comb out of her pocket, just like the real Christabell had in her handbag. The Ezzo clone began to warm up with some karate chopping. The Waldo clone growled and the Whiffy clone tried to stare the real one out.

"Get ready," the real Ezzo muttered to his real friends.

Suddenly he flew through the air, with a kung fu kick. The Ezzo clone leapt at the same time and they met in the middle!

The other clones launched attacks on their counterparts and a vicious fight began. As both sides were equally matched, the fight went on and on with no winners.

Suddenly the real Christabell managed to break away from her clone and flicked a dial on her 'get rid of black clouds' machine. She turned an arrow from 'black clouds' to 'black hearts' and hit the start button.

Can Christabell's machine save Monster City from the clone invasion? Pop on the start switch and see.

23 Active and passive

What an exciting fight! One way to make stories exciting is to use active voice sentences instead of passive voice sentences.

This is an active voice sentence:

The Christabell clone whipped a sharpened comb out of her pocket.

This is a passive voice sentence:

A sharpened comb was whipped out of the Christabell clone's pocket.

In the active voice sentence, the subject of the sentence (the Christabell clone) does the action (whipping the comb out of her pocket). In the passive voice sentence, the subject (the comb) is the thing that the action is done to (being whipped out of the pocket).

24 Double consonants

With all those mirror-image clones around, it was surprising people didn't get more confused than they did.

Some words with double letters can be almost as confusing to spell correctly.

hitting   bullying   terrorize   petty

Put a tick next to the active sentences in these pairs.

1 a◯ Christabell was glared at.
   b◯ The Ezzo clone glared at Christabell.

2 a◯ The Ezzo clone punched Ezzo.
   b◯ A punch was thrown at Ezzo.

3 a◯ Whiffy yelped.
   b◯ A yelp was heard.

4 a◯ Christabell was pushed to the ground.
   b◯ The Whiffy clone pushed Christabell to the ground.

5 a◯ The Waldo clone grabbed Ezzo's foot in his mouth.
   b◯ Ezzo's foot was grabbed.

6 a◯ Ezzo yanked the Waldo clone's ear.
   b◯ The Waldo clone's ear was yanked.

7 a◯ Ezzo helped Christabell up.
   b◯ Christabell was helped up.

8 a◯ Whiffy was jabbed in the back.
   b◯ The Christabell clone jabbed Whiffy in the back.

9 a◯ Everyone fought viciously.
   b◯ A vicious fight was started.

10 a◯ A hum was heard from Christabell's machine.
   b◯ Christabell's machine hummed.

Rewrite these passive sentences to turn them into active ones.

11 The Christabell clone was thumped by Christabell. _____

_____

12 The Whiffy clone was knocked out. _____

13 Ezzo was bitten by the Waldo clone. _____

14 A terrible smell was made by Whiffy. _____

15 The button was pushed. _____

Read these sentences and underline the word in bold that is spelt correctly.

1 Ezzo had a **sugestion suggestion suggesstion** to make – "Let's fight!"

2 "Any time you think it's **necessary neccesary neccessary**," shouted his clone.

3 "We'll find you some **acomodation accomodation accommodation** – in prison," Christabell said fiercely.

4 "I'd **recommend reccommend reccomend** you run away from the stink," sneered the Whiffy clone.

5 "I **suppose supose supposse** you think that's funny," Whiffy answered.

6 "Forget the **disscusion disscussion discussion** – let's get on with the fight," the Ezzo clone insisted.

7 "Just as well I've got the same **posessions possesions possessions** as you, dear original," said the Christabell clone, pulling out her sharpened comb.

8 Christabell slammed the comb down and said, "Now, now, wouldn't want anyone to have an **accident acident aciddent**, would we?"

9 "I'm just **begginning beginning begining** to fight," said her clone.

10 "I've a **conffesion confesion confession** to make," said Christabell. "I don't like you."

11 "And in **adition addition aditton**, I'm going to make sure you learn your lesson," she went on.

12 "We should never have **alowed allowed allowwed** this to get so far," said Ezzo.

13 "Nice **matress mattres mattress**," said the Whiffy clone, bouncing up and down on Whiffy's chest.

14 "I wish you'd just **disappear dissapear disapear**," Whiffy muttered between bounces.

15 "You're **officially oficially officialy** done for," said Christabell as she turned on the machine.

The machine began to hum and hiss. It started to suck the black-hearted clones towards it like a giant magnet for baddies, leaving the goodies behind.

The clones were lifted off the ground and although they tried to hold on to furniture, it yanked them into a tube. There was a loud noise, a 'pop', and four large bottles came out of the back of the machine. Inside each bottle was a trapped clone!

"Good. It works," the real Christabell remarked. "I thought it might be useful to bottle baddies as well as clouds."

Back at the palace P, Edgar and Flob were living in luxury. Cloned monsters rushed around, obeying their every command. "Oh, glorious Princess. Would you like another ice cream?" one asked, curtseying to the ground in front of P.

"My Lord Flob. Would you care for more sweets?" asked another.

"The clones I sent should have eliminated the Smile Street gang by now. We have no opposition left," Edgar smiled knowingly, as clones bowed around him.

(25) Parts of sentences

You need to be able to spot which parts of sentences are which.

For instance, verbs are words or groups of words that describe actions.

> run   was talking   will go   laughs

Adverbs describe verbs to tell us how they are being done

> quickly   sadly   politely   fast

Adjectives describe nouns.

> yellow   happy   dark   quiet   shrill

Pronouns replace nouns to make sentences read better.

> him   her   it   their

Prepositions tell us where things are placed in relation to one another.

> under   over   beside   outside

(26) Poetry

One of the cloned servants wrote a poem praising P, Edgar and Flob – but he made up some of the words! P couldn't understand them all and she snarled at the servant that he'd have to explain them.

Poets often use words in unusual ways. Sometimes they make up new words and use them in nonsense verses. They may make up new words that sound interesting, or as if they should have a particular meaning, or because they sound like two words put together.

Oh dear, Edgar is getting far too big for his boots! Let's see what the machine is going to do next - add on the whirly cogs.

Decide which parts of speech have been written in bold. Write verb, adjective, preposition, pronoun or adverb next to each sentence.

1   Ezzo **watched** the machine **work**.   _____

2   Only the **black-hearted** clones were captured by the **clever** machine.   _____

3   Christabell stood **next to** Ezzo.   _____

4   Christabell said **happily**, "My machine caught the clones **easily!**"   _____

5   The huge machine made a **loud** noise.   _____

6   "**Get** her! She's **running** away!" Christabell **yelled, pointing** at a clone.   _____

7   Whiffy shouted **angrily**, then ran **quickly** across the room.   _____

8   The bottles popped **out of** the back **of** the machine – each one
    had a clone **inside** it.   _____

9   A clone **grabbed** at a chair as he **flew** through the air.   _____

10 The Christabell clone shouted when the machine sucked **her** towards **it**.   _____

11 Ezzo hit his clone **hard** on the nose.   _____

12 One of the clones stood **on** a chair and another hid **under** the table.   _____

13 The **trapped** clones were really **angry**.   _____

14 The Ezzo clone beat his fists **against** the glass.   _____

15 A clone picked up a chair and threw **it** across the room, but **it** missed.   _____

Read the poem and then decide what some of the made-up words mean to you.

There once was a glorhumious Princess
called P,
Who wanted to rule Monster City, you see.
She was bright, she was bru and she thought of a
plan;
A plan that was clever and cru –
it was just the jan.
To rule Monster City with clones from a photo,
Clones that were cruel, mean, devy and doted
On glorhumious Princess P.

And Flob was all fumbly, jibbery and jumbly,
In case all their plans should go crumbly.
But that was a jear he should not have feared,
For the plan was zapzang, it appeared.
Glorhumious P and our skrivy Edgar;
They planned and they plotted much better,
Than ever was thought of by Flob.

1   I think **glorhumious** means

    _____

2   **bru** means _____

3   **cru** means _____

4   **jan** means _____

5   **devy** means _____

6   **fumbly** means _____

7   **jibbery** means _____

8   **jumbly** means _____

9   **jear** means _____

10 **zapzang** means _____

11 **skrivy** means _____

12 My favourite nonsense word is:

    _____

13 I like it best because _____

    _____

    _____

14 My least favourite nonsense word is:

    _____

15 I like it least because _____

    _____

    _____

P was reaching out for her fourth ice cream, when the clone carrying it began to slide backwards across the floor. Suddenly all the cloned monsters were lifted off their feet and, although they tried to hold on to curtains and tables, they began flying out of doors and windows. Christabell's machine was working busily. Because it sucked up black hearts, it also began to pull at P and Edgar.

"Help!" Edgar shouted, as he flew out of the window and clung to a tree branch. His trousers were pulled into the machine first, revealing his purple spotted underwear. Then he was pulled in and emerged out of the other end in a bottle.

P started to scream, but the machine sucked up the scream's powers as well as P herself. She, too, was left squashed inside a bottle, where she screamed herself hoarse.

Flob wasn't sucked up, though. He didn't have a black heart, only bad habits taught to him by P and Edgar.

27 Spelling rules

P was a bit bored with some of her clones, so she decided that only the cloned monster servants who could pass a spelling test would keep their jobs.

Would you pass the test?

Remember that many spellings follow patterns – if you can see the pattern, you can guess the spelling.

28 Speech tags

After a while, the Monster City police came to talk to everyone, including all the people who'd seen the fight. Some people were upset; others were amazed; a few – including P and Edgar – were angry.

When you write dialogue, you can show how people are feeling by what they say, but you can also use speech tags to show how they say it. Speech tags are words that mean 'said'.

It's a shame P didn't deafen herself with all that screaming and then Monster City might get some peace and quiet. Put the squasher sticker on.

Underline the words that are spelt incorrectly. To help you, all the words in each group follow the same spelling rule.

1   receive ceiling concieted deceitful
2   monkeys turkies donkeys alleys
3   likeing rattling writing closing
4   tries carries dies spys
5   niece piece anceint friend
6   flying dying hurrying marrieing
7   hopeful peaceful careful fatful
8   taking liking behaveing coping
9   lovly nicely closely falsely

10 warily easily mightyly nastily
11 hummed pinned pated batted
12 fashionning returning disturbing trusting
13 neighbour weigh sleigh riegn
14 patches witchs catches ditches
15 leaves elves calfs rooves

Match the things people said with suitable speech tags from the box. You won't need them all, but you might decide to use some of them more than once.

> boasted whispered answered muttered admitted screeched murmured retorted shouted called snarled begged yelled bellowed roared grunted screamed reported asked replied queried snapped whined insisted said

1   "What can you tell me about the fight?" _____ the police officer.
2   "I wish I'd never got involved," _____ Flob.
3   "You idiot," _____ P.
4   "The first strange thing was the swimming pool being smashed up," _____ Ezzo.
5   "The inventing competition was quite a good idea," _____ Christabell. "It did keep me busy!"
6   "Please don't tell Edgar or P I said that," _____ Flob.
7   "I thought Ezzo was behaving oddly, because he was rude to me," _____ Christabell.
8   "For a while I was really upset with Christabell," _____ Ezzo.
9   "Just let me get at my so-called original and I'll show him who's best," _____ the Ezzo clone.
10 "Since you ask, I'm fine," P _____.
11 "I still think we're better than they are," _____ the Christabell clone.
12 "I just do everything P tells me to," the Ezzo clone _____
13 "It was me who went to the Science Museum and found Ivor Bigbrain tied up," _____ Whiffy.
14 "Let me out of this bottle!" _____ Edgar.
15 "Next time, we'll win!" P _____.

Flob spent the next three days pulling Edgar and P out of the unbreakable bottles. It took ages because they could only squeeze out bit by bit, with the help of soap rubbed on their heads and faces to make them slippery.

When they did eventually pop out, they went away to hide for a while.

Flob missed getting extra bags of sweets from the clones, but with P and Edgar away he found other monsters were nice to him and let him share their sweets anyway.

Christabell helped Ezzo plan a birthday picnic. When the day came, she switched on her 'get rid of black clouds' machine, but unfortunately P's scream had damaged it and it didn't work properly. It rained all day, but Ezzo didn't mind. He danced between the raindrops.

"I'm celebrating with my real friends and that's good enough for me!" he smiled.

29 Vivid writing

To make your writing vivid, you can use adverbs to describe the action that's happening.

Ezzo walked towards his clone.

You could write:

Ezzo walked **angrily** towards his clone.

Sometimes it's even more interesting to use vivid verbs instead.

Ezzo **strode** towards his clone.

30 Punctuation

Colons are usually used at the start of a list or an explanation.

People P doesn't like: Ezzo, Christabell, Waldo and Whiffy.

Semi-colons are used to separate two parts of a sentence, instead of a connective. They can also be used to separate items on a list.

The Christabell clone was mean; P liked her.

Parenthetic commas, brackets and dashes can all be used to insert extra information. Dashes can also be used to add an afterthought to a sentence.

P read the article about being nice to people – she didn't like it at all.

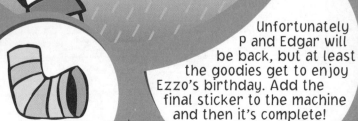

Unfortunately P and Edgar will be back, but at least the goodies get to enjoy Ezzo's birthday. Add the final sticker to the machine and then it's complete!

The Monster City police finally managed to write a report about what had happened. It was very clear, but it wasn't very exciting. Underline the verb in bold that you think completes the sentence in the most vivid way possible.

1 Flob told the police that he and some friends took hammers and **hit smashed whacked** the swimming pool walls.

2 Christabell was **happy excited overjoyed** when she heard about the inventing competition.

3 She was **annoyed irritated cross** when the rules kept changing.

4 Ezzo was **angry furious annoyed** when Christabell was rude to him.

5 He was **bewildered upset amazed**, because it was so unlike her.

6 Waldo and Whiffy **walked crept sneaked** through the Science Museum.

7 They **found discovered encountered** Ivor Bigbrain, who was tied up in his office.

8 He **explained described recounted** what P and Edgar intended to do.

9 Meanwhile, Ezzo had gone home and had **talked argued rowed** with Christabell.

10 Whiffy and Waldo **persuaded asked convinced** Ezzo to go back to the Science Museum with them.

11 Once he **realised believed understood** what was going on, he told Christabell about it.

12 Just then, the clones turned up and **picked demanded requested** a fight.

13 The Ezzo clone **hit punched struck** Ezzo.

14 Christabell **slipped ran hurried** away and started her machine.

15 The clones were **conquered beaten overwhelmed**.

Use colons, semi-colons, parenthetic commas, brackets or dashes to punctuate these sentences about life in Monster City. Sometimes, part of the punctuation has been done.

1 There were several recipes for teatime treats for monsters on the recipe pages dragon delights; sphinx sundaes; giant jellies; and fairy flapjacks.

2 There were three kinds of competition quizzes, crosswords, and colouring-in.

3 There was a picture of a green handbag with yellow handles P decided to buy it.

4 There were adverts in the magazine for crowns with jewels rose-tinted spectacles books of instructions for ruling the world and P's favourite chocolates.

5 There was a letters page, but it was boring, so P skipped it.

6 The editor, who was called Jix had written a letter to the readers.

7 P read the first article (it was about ghosts then flipped to the horoscopes.

8 The magazine had three articles about hairstyles P only liked one) and one about which shoes to wear.

9 P read very fast – after all, she was very clever but could hardly remember anything about the magazine once she had finished it.

10 P decided that Jix the editor – was stupid because he said people should be nice to each other.

11 P flicked through the magazine looking for pictures she liked movie stars best.

12 P tried to do the crossword, but it was too hard she gave up quickly.

13 P could see Flob walking around outside she ignored him and read the magazine.

14 P's horoscope for the day 'Be careful not to get sucked into anything you don't like and don't get stuck in a tight spot!'

15 P got very excited the magazine said Sumi Spangles the popstar was coming to Monster City.

Answers

Test 1 Metaphors and similes
Answers such as
1. glass, S
2. a tin of sardines, S
3. dirty snowdrifts, M
4. milk, S
5. skyscrapers, M
6. stars, S
7. tar, S
8. dropped playing cards, M
9. a dolphin, S
10. stalactites, M
11. jagged teeth, M
12. stone, M
13. a beetroot, S
14. beached whale, M
15. swatted wasp, S

Test 2 Root words
1. two – bi
2. study - ology
3. hear - audi
4. air - aero
5. fear - phobia
6. water - aqua
7. before - pre
8. self - auto
9. belive - cred
10. to write - graph
11. first - prim
12. greater - super
13. three - tri
14. to write - scribe
15. across - trans

Test 3 Language
1. formal
2. informal
3. formal
4. formal
5. informal
6. informal
7. informal
8. formal
9. formal
10. informal
11. formal
12. informal
13. informal
14. formal
15. informal

Test 4 Spelling
1. incorrectly
2. announced
3. interrupted
4. companion
5. completing
6. automatically
7. sentences
8. invention
9. something
10. probably
11. leaflet
12. competition
13. explained
14. swimming
15. understanding

Test 5 Comprehension
Your finished intructions should look like this:

The Science Museum Invention Competition Rules (New)
1. Read the rules and bin them. ✓
2. Put signed invention plan ✗ in an envelope. Attach name and address label ★ with sticky tape, not glue
3. ③ Entries must fit into a crate 3m long ✗ 2m deep × 3m wide unless you have special permission for a larger entry - send write to us for For 5QXb1.   off today
4. Use glow in the dark ink to label buttons on your entry. ↖
5. Instructions must be typed in English ← on white paper.
6. Spend no more than 500 Doobreys Borrow and put all signed ✗ receipts in the   money envelope with your entry form.   from Ezzo

Test 6 Proof-reading
1. Extra Science Museum Invention Competition Rules.
2. These are the new extra rules of the competition. Follow them or your entry will be disqualified.
3. Your entry must fall into one of these groups: Making Things; Art; Transport; Having Fun; Doing Boring Things For Us; Food and Drink; Helping The Environment.
4. There are special rules for each category. Follow them or else!
5. Inventions that make things must use recyclable materials. The invention must be bigger than whatever it makes.
6. Art includes painting, sculpting, writing and music. Any other kind of art comes under Having Fun, unless its boring or sad, when it will be disqualified.
7. The art your invention makes must make people happy, or it will be disqualified.
8. All kinds of transport are allowed, except those that take people to impossible places like over the rainbow.
9. If your invention goes so fast it makes the judges sick, or so slow they fall asleep, it will be disqualified.
10. Having Fun can include anything you like, but if the judges get bored, your invention will be disqualified.
11. Doing Boring Things For Us includes housework, homework etc, but only the boring kinds. If the judges don't think your invention does something boring, it will be disqualified.
12. Food and Drink includes machines that grow food, invent recipes or cook. The judges will taste the food. If they die of food poisoning your invention will be disqualified.
13. Helping the Environment. This includes inventions that recycle materials, cut waste or help people save energy. If the judges waste a lot of energy understanding your invention, it will be disqualified.
14. You will lose marks if you bore the judges.
15. No bribery allowed. Not even chocolate. Really.

Test 7 Fact and fiction
1. fact
2. fiction
3. fiction
4. fact
5. opinion
6. fact
7. opinion
8. fact
9. fiction
10. fact
11. opinion
12. fiction
13. opinion
14. fiction
15. opinion

Test 8 Crosswords
Across
1. generous
4. dishonest
5. placid
8. caring
10. daft
11. resent
12. unhelpful
13. tough
14. despairing
15. intelligence

Down
1. grumpy
2. spite
3. kind
6. cheerful
7. truthful
9. gratitude

Test 9 Sayings
1. A bird in the hand is worth (d) two in the bush.
2. People who live in glass houses (e) shouldn't throw stones.
3. Familiarity breeds (a) contempt.
4. Absence makes the heart (h) grow fonder.
5. Out of sight, (j) out of mind.
6. He who hesitates (l) lost.
7. If you make your bed, (b) you must lie in it.
8. A rose by any other name would smell (o) as sweet.
9. You might as well be hanged for a sheep (f) as a lamb.
10. In for a penny, in for (m) a pound.
11. Look before (c) you leap.
12. A friend in need is (n) a friend indeed.
13. Cut your coat according to (i) your cloth.
14. Better late (k) than never.
15. The early bird catches (g) the worm.

Test 10 Letters
1. writing
2. happened
3. while
4. skateboarding
5. probably
6. wrong
7. nasty
8. sorry
9. sure
10. have
11. friends
12. still
13. shouting
14. should
15. apologise

Test 11 Weighing things up
Until today, Christabell and I have always been good friends. She has always been on my side in fights, specially with P and Edgar. I think we have a lot in common, even though she likes working on her computer and I like skateboarding and stuff like that. We like the same kind of jokes, and we both like Whiffy and Waldo. It seems to me that nothing has happened to change any of that.
However, I'm not sure Christabell agrees with me. On one hand, she was really rude and mean to me when I saw her in the park. I can't think why she would call me selfish for wanting help with my party, when I don't think she has been selfish working on her invention. Then again, maybe she was just in a bad mood or something, because she seemed okay when I spoke to her just now!

Test 12 Conjunctions
1. Christabell and Ezzo were good friends, but she started being nasty to him.
2. If Ezzo is hurt, he should say so.
3. When Ezzo saw Christabell in the park, she was with some new friends.
4. Christabell was friendly, then she changed.
5. Either something is wrong with Christabell or Ezzo is imagining things.
6. If Ezzo is sad, he sulks.
7. Ezzo stormed out because he was upset.
8. Ezzo was upset, so he stormed out.
9. Ezzo didn't want to argue, so he ran off.
10. Christabell wanted to show Ezzo her invention, but he slammed the door.
11. Christabell saw Ezzo while he was skateboarding in the park.
12. When Ezzo got home, he was still angry.
13. As Christabell spoke to Ezzo, she realised he was annoyed with her.
14. While Christabell was inventing, Ezzo was skateboarding in the park.
15. Ezzo was hurt, but he smiled bravely.

Test 13 Spelling
1. separate
2. telephone
3. disappear
4. library
5. probably
6. important
7. garage
8. pleasant
9. fasten
10. necklace
11. elephant
12. fashion
13. brother
14. seventy
15. necessary